BASIC/NOT BORING
LANGUAGE SKILLS

WRITING

Grades 4-5

Inventive Exercises to Sharpen
Skills and Raise Achievement

Series Concept & Development
by Imogene Forte & Marjorie Frank

Exercises by Marjorie Frank

Illustrations by Kathleen Bullock

Incentive Publications, Inc.
Nashville, Tennessee

Thank you to the fourth and fifth graders who contributed pieces of original writing to be used in this book, and thank you to poet David May, who inspired many of the writers during his sessions with them as a "Poet in Residence" at Briscoe and Helman Schools in Ashland, Oregon.

These pieces are used by permission from the writers.

page 14   Tahli O'Grady for "Coffee"

Page 37   Elizabeth Psomas for "I Am a Pot"
           Angela DiGorgo for "The River Sings"
           Jordan Jameson for "The Wind"
           Jennifer Gray for "My Toaster"
           Nelson Kling for "Rock Bridges"

page 38   Kayla Bryant for "Losing a Friend"
           Simone Wren for "Poets are like . . ." and "Falling through space is like . . ."
           Ariana Lewis for "Math is a hurricane . . ."
           Matthew Bianca for "When my little brother is angry . . ." and "Writing a new story is like . .
           Tessah Joseph for "The scratching of a pencil is like . . ."
           Laura Arndt for "Life is like a dark pool of water . . ."
           Rachael Wanderscheid for "Math problems are like . . ."
           Camille Morris for "Life is like a gift . . ." and "Life is like . . ."
           Greg Cross for "A Kid in Class"
           Jamie Cross for "I Am the Universe"

About the cover:
    Bound resist, or tie dye, is the most ancient known method
    of fabric surface design. The brilliance of the basic tie dye
    design on this cover reflects the possibilities that emerge
    from the mastery of basic skills.

Cover art by Mary Patricia Deprez, dba Tye Dye Mary®
Cover design by Marta Drayton, Joe Shibley, and W. Paul Nance
Edited by Anna Quinn and Tama Montgomery

ISBN 0-86530-402-5

PRINTED IN THE UNITED STATES OF AMERICA

TABLE OF CONTENTS

CELEBRATE BASIC LANGUAGE SKILLS

Basic does not mean boring! There certainly is nothing dull about . . .
   . . . watching a daring adventurer ride a barrel over Niagara Falls
   . . . writing with words that move around like snakes and tornadoes
   . . . concocting sentences that make your stomach flip
   . . . interviewing someone who's been struck by lightning or caught in a flying bathtub
   . . . digging up words to make a person's mouth water
   . . . tracking down courtroom impostors or tackling unsolved mysteries
   . . . finding that Jack Sprat and his wife have turned up in today's news
   . . . wondering why ships and planes disappear in the Bermuda Triangle
   . . . untangling an octopus and a squid or coming face-to-face with a shark

These are just some of the adventures students will explore as they celebrate basic language skills. The idea of celebrating the basics is just what it sounds like—enjoying and improving the skills of writing. Each page invites learners to try a high-interest, appealing exercise that will sharpen one specific writing skill. This is no ordinary fill-in-the-blanks way to learn! These exercises are fun and surprising. Students will do the useful work of practicing writing skills while they enjoy the interesting adventures of the curious and clever reporters for SPARK magazine. And, at the same time they practice basic writing skills, they will be sharpening thinking skills and many other language skills.

The pages in this book can be used in many ways:
   • for individual students to review or practice a particular skill
   • to sharpen the skill with a small or large group
   • by students working on their own
   • by students working under the direction of an adult

Each page may be used to introduce a new skill, reinforce a skill, or assess a student's ability to perform a skill. And there's more than just the great student activity pages. You'll also find an appendix filled with resources for students and teachers—including a ready-to-use test for assessing writing skills. The pages are written with the assumption that an adult will be available to assist the students with their learning and practice.

As your students take on the challenges of these adventures with writing, they will grow! And as you watch them check off the basic language skills they've strengthened, you can celebrate with them!

The Skills Test
   Use the skills test beginning on page 58 as a pretest and/or a post-test. This will help you check the students' mastery of basic writing skills and will prepare them for success on achievement tests.

SKILLS CHECKLIST FOR
WRITING, Grades 4-5

✔	SKILL	PAGE(S)
	Recognize and use effective words (specific, unusual, colorful, active, etc.)	10–16
	Recognize and replace overused or ordinary words and phrases	10–12
	Recognize and choose precise words for accurate meaning and interest	12, 13
	Recognize and use active rather than passive words	12
	Arrange words within sentences for clarity and an interesting sound	12, 19
	Identify poetry; use writing skills to write poetry	14, 15, 54
	Recognize and choose words that produce strong visual images	14, 15, 54
	Recognize and include sensory appeal in writing	14–16, 54
	Recognize and write clear, interesting sentences	17–24
	Recognize and create fluent sentences and paragraphs	17, 18, 20–24, 36, 44–53
	Infuse personal flavor into a selection	18, 53
	Revise sentences for clarity	19
	Revise writing for clarity, sequence, or effectiveness	19, 23, 32, 52
	Recognize and write clear questions	20, 21
	Recognize and create strong beginnings	22, 23
	Recognize and create strong endings	24, 25
	Recognize and create strong titles	26, 27
	Recognize and show clear organization within a written piece	28, 29
	Recognize and supply plenty of interesting, relevant details to a written idea	28, 29, 45, 46
	Recognize and use enough examples to support the main idea well	28–31
	Recognize and include details that are surprising, unusual, or extraordinary	29, 44–46
	Recognize and eliminate excess or unrelated details	30, 31
	Recognize and eliminate repetitive or unnecessary words, phrases, or sentences	30–31
	Recognize and arrange sentences for proper sequence and interesting sound	32, 33
	Recognize and write sentences of varied length and structure	33
	Adapt form, style, or content for a specific purpose	34, 35
	Adapt form and content for a specific audience	36
	Recognize a clear main idea; create pieces that clearly reveal the main idea	36, 44–53
	Recognize and write selections that have a clear beginning, middle, and end	36, 44–53
	Recognize and include literary techniques to make writing effective	37–41
	Recognize and include personification in writing	37
	Recognize and include metaphors, similes, and other figurative language in writing	38–41
	Recognize and include dialogue in writing	42
	Recognize and choose words and phrases to create a specific mood	43
	Recognize expository writing; use writing skills to write an expository selection	44
	Recognize and write good connections between ideas or parts of ideas	44
	Recognize imaginative writing; use writing skills to write an imaginative selection	45, 46
	Recognize persuasive selections; use writing skills to write a persuasive selection	47
	Recognize characterization; use writing skills to write a characterization	48, 49
	Recognize descriptive writing; use writing skills to write a descriptive selection	50, 51
	Identify opinions; use writing skills to write personal opinions	52, 53

WRITING

Skills Exercises

WRITING WITH A SPARK

Investigative reporters Charlie Scoop and Murphy Green work for a new magazine, SPARK. They investigate all kinds of stories and write enticing pieces for the top-selling magazine. Today, Charlie and Murphy are polishing sentences by replacing dull words with better ones.

Look at each word that has been crossed out. Find another word that says the same thing, but is much more colorful, sparkling, interesting, or unusual.

Just after the bank robbery, the police came ~~walking~~ into the bank.

People had ~~scared~~ looks on their faces. They were ~~shaking~~.

The fingernails tapping against the window glass ~~hurt~~ my ears.

It was a ~~dark~~ afternoon and the wind was ~~blowing~~.

How could this ~~funny~~ worm get inside my ~~perfect~~ apple?

Three strange characters came ~~slipping~~ down the stairs to the subway.

Pass me some of that ~~tasty~~ hot fudge!

The comet ~~moved~~ across the night sky with amazing speed.

A ~~big~~ avalanche surprised and ~~worried~~ the skiers.

MURPHY GREEN

Use with page 11.

Name

10

WRITING WITH A SPARK, CONT.

Look at each word that has been crossed out. Replace it with another word with a similar meaning that is much more specific, colorful, interesting, or unusual.

The family had to run for their lives as the ~~awful~~ storm approached.

Have you ever watched ~~busy~~ snowboarders do their tricks?

You'll never believe the ~~awful~~ color of the dress she was wearing!

I have never seen waves as ~~big~~ as the ones I rode today!

Have you ever heard the ~~interesting~~ sound of a tornado coming?

Sirens ~~sounded~~ as the fire engines ~~went~~ toward the burning school.

How would you describe the ~~bad~~ taste of this ~~old~~ sandwich?

This wasn't the first time that the ~~little~~ chimp had been in trouble.

Catch the act! See the ~~funny~~ gorilla juggle ~~big~~ chairs at the zoo today.

It must have been ~~scary~~ to come face-to-face with Bigfoot.

The escaped elephant, ~~happy~~ to be free, ~~went~~ across the freeway.

Huge waves ~~moved~~ closer to the house.

Three ~~big~~ walruses came ~~crawling~~ across the beach.

~~Good~~ syrup slowly ~~moved~~ over my pancakes.

CHARLIE SCOOP

Use with page 10.

Name

CATCH THE ACTION!

Murphy got to her assignment late—just as the Circus Parade was getting started. It was such a lively, fun parade. The photographer did not get there in time to take photos, so Murphy wrote about all the action going on. Take a close look at each sentence she has written in her notebook. Her sentences need to show more action. Rewrite the sentences to better describe the parade. Change verbs such as *came* and *went* into more active verbs. Remember, the reader wants to be able to actually picture the actions in the parade!

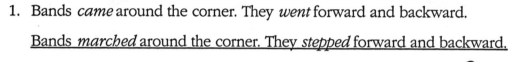

1. Bands *came* around the corner. They *went* forward and backward.

   Bands *marched* around the corner. They *stepped* forward and backward.

2. The clowns walked down the street in their huge, floppy feet.

   _____

3. Baton twirlers came along behind the dancing bears.

   _____

4. Clowns in frog costumes were on pogo sticks.

   _____

5. We ate all kinds of scrumptious food.

   _____

6. We looked at the people who bungee jumped off the skyscraper.

   _____

7. Huge, multicolored hot air balloons were overhead.

   _____

8. Salsa dancers came by as the band played catchy music.

   _____

9. Balls were in the air in front of the jugglers.

   _____

10. Fire-eaters used sticks of flames in their acts.

    _____

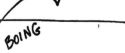

Name _____

PRECISELY PRECARIOUS

Murphy doesn't want to miss this story! Barnaby Bolder is going over Niagara Falls in an old barrel! When she writes the story, she needs to use words that tell precisely what happened. Her readers will want to know!

Choose a word from this page to finish Murphy's sentences and phrases. Use a word that fits the phrase precisely.

1. the _____ roar of the falls ahead

2. a _____ smell inside the barrel

3. Barnaby's _____ ride

4. The barrel _____ over the edge.

5. What a _____ character!

6. _____ rocks waiting at the bottom

7. Would you trust this _____ barrel?

8. caught in the _____ water

9. a _____ 200-foot drop

10. a _____ adventurer

11. the _____ barrel

12. Barnaby's _____ stomach

13. the _____ space inside the barrel

14. the _____ crowd watching the fall

15. the _____ power of the water

16. Barnaby's _____ body after the fall

terrified

unbelievable

turbulent

wild

jagged

cramped

perilous

steep

foolish

damp

threatening

moldy

CRAZY

sturdy

rushing fearless awestruck

nervous

NAUSEOUS WHIRLING

MIGHTY

swirling

battered

deafening

RECKLESS

threatening

treacherous

PLUMMETS

plunging

NICE SHOT!

WOW!

Name _____

Basic Skills/Writing 4-5

WORDS ON THE MOVE

The words just don't seem to want to sit still on the page today! They keep winding and moving all over. Murphy is preparing a page with writing that looks as if it were painted on the page instead of written in nice, neat lines. You could call this *painted* writing!

Read the page. Then choose one of the ideas from the Idea File, and try some painted writing of your own. Use another piece of paper.

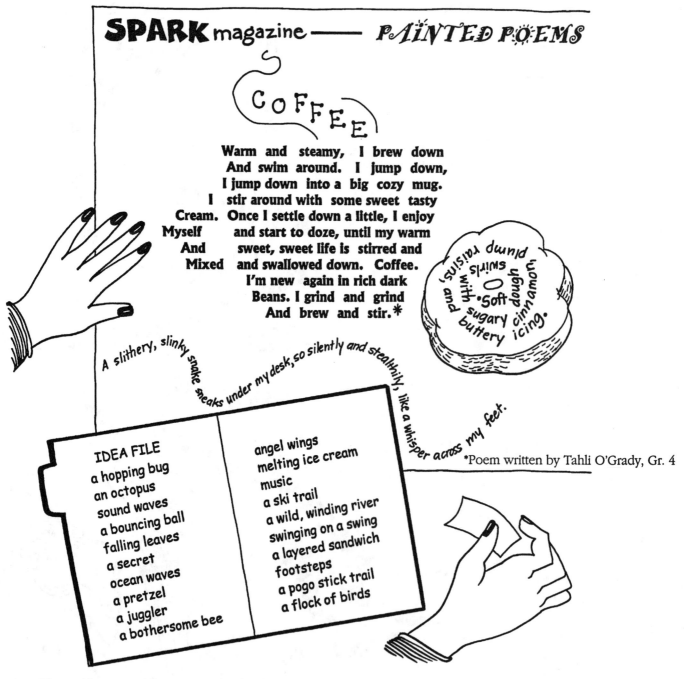

SPARK magazine ——— *PAINTED POEMS*

COFFEE

Warm and steamy, I brew down
And swim around. I jump down,
I jump down into a big cozy mug.
I stir around with some sweet tasty
Cream. Once I settle down a little, I enjoy
Myself   and start to doze, until my warm
And   sweet, sweet life is stirred and
Mixed   and swallowed down. Coffee.
I'm new again in rich dark
Beans. I grind and grind
And brew and stir.*

A slithery, slinky snake sneaks under my desk, so silently and stealthily, like a whisper across my feet.

*Poem written by Tahli O'Grady, Gr. 4

IDEA FILE
a hopping bug
an octopus
sound waves
a bouncing ball
falling leaves
a secret
ocean waves
a pretzel
a juggler
a bothersome bee

angel wings
melting ice cream
music
a ski trail
a wild, winding river
swinging on a swing
a layered sandwich
footsteps
a pogo stick trail
a flock of birds

Use with page 15.

Name

WEATHERED WORDS

When Charlie goes out on an assignment to cover wild weather, his words become turbulent, too. They start taking the shape of lightning and tornadoes!

Choose one of the weather topics, and make a painted writing piece about it in the space below. Make the shape of the words match the topic.

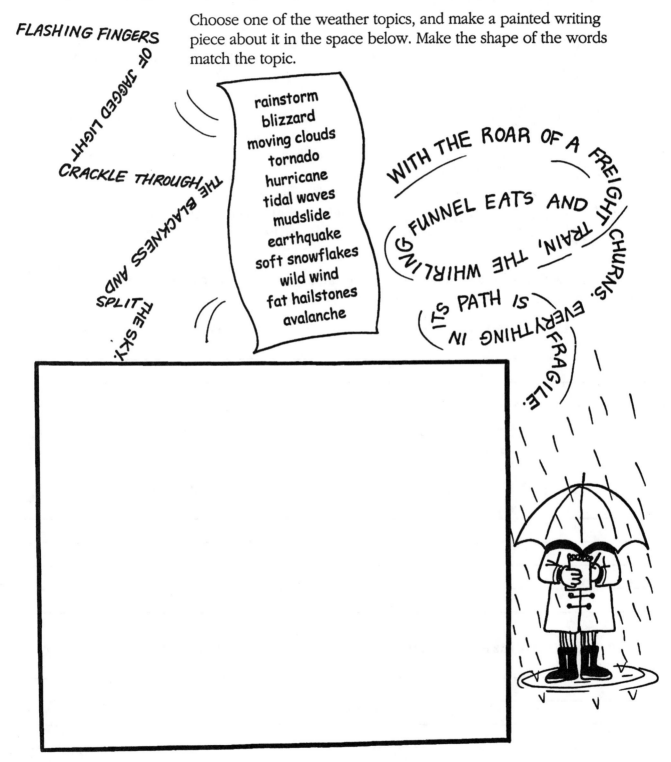

FLASHING FINGERS OF JAGGED LIGHT CRACKLE THROUGH THE BLACKNESS AND SPLIT THE SKY.

rainstorm
blizzard
moving clouds
tornado
hurricane
tidal waves
mudslide
earthquake
soft snowflakes
wild wind
fat hailstones
avalanche

WITH THE ROAR OF A FREIGHT TRAIN, THE WHIRLING FUNNEL EATS AND CHURNS EVERYTHING IN ITS PATH IS FRAGILE.

Use with page 14.

Name

WORDS WITH TASTE

When is a hamburger not just a plain old hamburger?—when it's time to write about it in a food review for the magazine. Charlie digs up the tastiest words he can think of to write about the hamburgers at The Big Cheese Drive-in.

Try the mouthwatering burger, dripping with charbroiled flavors! It's wrapped in creamy melted cheddar and crisp fresh bacon. Then it's drenched with your choice of buttery fried onions, crisp and tangy dill pickles, plump tomato slices, or crunchy green lettuce—all nestled inside a soft, fresh-from-the-oven, home-baked bun.

Help Charlie with his food reviews. For each food, list several mouthwatering phrases he can use to tempt readers to rush right out to The Big Cheese!

Hot Fudge Sundae

Spaghetti with Meatballs

Deep-Dish Apple Pie

Stack of Pancakes

Fried Chicken Dinner

You choose a food!

Name _____

16

GOOD ADVICE

Murphy writes an advice column under the name of "Aunt Lucinda." Today she is advising readers about things they should be careful never to do. She has started with a list of ideas for her column. Now she is turning some of the phrases from her list into interesting, complete sentences.

Aunt Lucinda's Advice
Don't ever...
talk back to your mother
save an ice cream bar in your pocket
forget to pay your taxes
go into a burning building
try to interview the gorilla at the zoo
wear your pajamas to work
stand on top of a bridge in the wind
eat a sandwich without mayonnaise
swallow peach pits

AUNT LUCINDA (a.k.a. Murphy Green)

Dear Readers:
• If you're asked to interview a gorilla, quickly reply, "Never!"
• Maude's husband, Bob, will probably never wear his pajamas to work again!
• My niece learned a lesson the last time she swallowed a peach pit. I don't think she will do it again.

List some things you think people should never do. (You may need to use extra paper.) Then take eight of your ideas and expand them into interesting sentences. Be sure to include at least one declarative, one imperative, and one exclamatory sentence.

1. _____
2. _____
3. _____
4. _____
5. _____
6. _____
7. _____
8. _____

Name

FEATURE YOURSELF

Charlie is going to be the featured reporter in next month's issue of SPARK magazine. This is a monthly column where readers can get to know some personal information about one of the reporters. You can be the feature of this page, too. Finish the same sentences Charlie will finish. Make sure that the words you write make each sentence clear and interesting.

My greatest fear is a big hairy spider. I'd like to be emperor of my own island someday ...and,...

ABOUT MYSELF

1. Once, I _____

    _____, but I probably will never do that again.

2. It wasn't too long ago that I _____ .

3. The greatest thing about me is _____ .

4. I wish I could _____ .

5. Wild horses could not drag me to _____ .

6. Last year, I _____ .

7. Yesterday, I _____ .

8. _____ is my greatest fear.

9. Nothing makes me madder than _____ !

10. If I could change something in the world, it would be _____

    _____ .

11. I think _____ .

12. In 10 years, I expect to be _____ .

13. I would really like to try _____ .

14. Something else fascinating about me is _____ .

Name

18

STOMACH-FLIPPING NEWS

Today's hot news is the stomach-flipping, nerve-wracking, crowd-pleasing new *CYCLONE-LAND AMUSEMENT PARK*. It just opened yesterday, and crowds are flocking to try the thrilling rides. After Charlie tried a few for his report, his sentences got a bit scrambled. They don't say exactly what he means! *(For example, in #1—he seems to be saying that the stomachache was riding The Corkscrew!)* Clear up the confusion! Rewrite each sentence so that its meaning is clear.

1. While riding **The Corkscrew** for the third time, a stomachache bothered me.

   _____

2. As a child, my dad took me on roller coasters every weekend.

   _____

3. I'll write about the pirates who robbed ships in the magazine.

   _____

4. While riding **The Plunge,** the wind picked up.

   _____

5. A clown sold cold ice cream bars to the children with sprinkles.

   _____

6. Some teenagers were banned from **The Train of Terror** after breaking the rules by the manager.

   _____

7. After fainting on the ride through **The Python's Den,** the kids worried that their mother would never recover.

   _____

8. Having fallen off her seat into **The Raging River,** the students tried to pull their teacher back into the raft.

   _____

9. To save money for a day at the amusement park, Mrs. Burton hired Tim and Tom to clean her garage.

   _____

10. Last, I visited the **Haunted Mansion** beside the ticket booth that was very scary.

   _____

Name

ASK ME ANYTHING!

If you want to find out something, you need to ask the right questions. Good reporters ask good questions. They plan their questions before they go investigating, so that they will know exactly what to ask.

> Excuse me, sir. Do you speak English?
>
> No, do you speak Martian?

Think about the questions you would ask to find out interesting information about the people or events on pages 20 and 21. Get ready for some interviews by writing down the questions. Write clear, complete questions that ask exactly what you want to know! Write at least four good questions to ask each person.

1. a lion tamer _____

_____

_____

_____

2. a terrorist's hostage _____

_____

_____

_____

3. a high school student _____

_____

_____

_____

Use with page 21.

Name _____

20

ASK ME ANYTHING! CONT.

Get ready for some interviews by writing down the questions. Write clear, complete questions that ask exactly what you want to know!

4. *a rock star* _____

_____

_____

_____

5. *a 100-year-old person* _____

_____

_____

_____

6. *a witness to a robbery* _____

_____

_____

_____

7. *someone who's been struck by lightning* _____

_____

_____

_____

Use with page 20.

Name _____

BETTER BEGINNINGS

Reporters know that a beginning needs to grab the reader. Whether it is a story, an essay, an article, or a report—the beginning is important. If a beginning is dull, the reader may give up right there. So Charlie is trying some different beginnings for his report on last night's school board meeting, where middle school students staged a protest. Which beginning do you think is best?

GREASY GRUB IS GROSS!

BETTER CHOW NOW!

Some Ash Middle School students protested at the school board meeting.

Students demanded that the school board discuss the poor lunches.

No one could remember a school board meeting like this one.

There were fireworks at the school board meeting last night.

Who dared to deliver rotting meat loaf and slimy Jell-o™ to a school board meeting?

"Down with bad lunches!" was the cry heard at the school board meeting.

Rewrite each of these beginnings to make them more attention grabbing.

1. The food in the school cafeteria is pretty awful. _____
   _____

2. It was an average day in July. _____
   _____

3. Andrea left for school at 8 o'clock. _____
   _____

4. In the summer of 1969, American astronauts walked on the moon. _____
   _____

5. My mom got a new hairstyle, and she asked my opinion of it. _____
   _____

6. One day after school, Dan and his friends sat around with nothing to do. _____
   _____

7. School starts at 8:30 A.M. _____
   _____

8. There are many earthquakes every day._____
   _____

9. Jamie asked me to take care of her pet skunk. _____
   _____

Name _____

22

SMASHING BEGINNINGS

Murphy wants the beginnings of all her writing pieces to be smashing! Of course, the beginning is the first thing that "hits" the reader, so it's a good idea to make it smashing, exciting, bold, catchy, fantastic, or outrageous!

Good-bye to 100-Year-Old Structure

A massive ball of steel has turned little red Firehouse 5 into dust and flying fragments!

Choose eight of the topics below, or invent some of your own. Write a smashing sentence to begin each writing piece. Use a separate piece of paper.

a description of a spooky house

a friend in big trouble

a mysterious visitor

NEW RULES AT YOUR SCHOOL

a disappearing teacher

how to clean your room

an outrageous mistake

TRAVEL IN A TIME MACHINE

A MEMORY FROM LONG AGO

your most embarrassing moment

the reason for lightning

a major argument with your brother (or sister)

convincing someone to try salami cantelope bubblegum

convincing someone that you saw something unbelievable

Name

WRAPPING IT UP

At last, Bartholomew Gerkins had been found. After a mysterious five-year disappearance, he was returned to his family. Everything was finally back to normal. Only his little daughter still wondered. As she watched him write in his journal, she said to herself, "I was so sure my dad was left-handed like me!"

The End

Do you like mysterious endings like this one, where you are not really sure how things turned out? Imaginative endings are great fun to write. It's important to have strong endings. After all, that's the last thing the reader sees!

With a good ending you can . . .

. . . totally surprise the reader

. . . give an unexpected solution

. . . tie up all the loose ends

. . . ask a question or answer a question

. . . finish an explanation

. . . solve a problem

. . . make the reader laugh

. . . teach a lesson

. . . leave the reader looking forward to your next story

. . . leave the reader with a mystery

These are some of my best endings, if I do say so myself!

MURPHY GREEN

And that was the end of that...or was it?

The magician whispered to himself, "I'll never try that trick again."

Of course, the second act was yet to come.

I wonder what will happen on next year's field trip!

At least that's the story we told our parents.

She was lucky to escape with her life!

Eat it with whipped cream or chocolate sauce, but never with gravy!

The next day, we had a new substitute.

Would you ever shop at that store?

You can imagine what our report cards looked like!

Practice writing good endings of your own. Use the spaces on the next page (page 25) to write a sample ending for each piece of writing described.

Use with page 25.

Name

WRAPPING IT UP, CONT.

Write a strong ending that might be used for each of the writing examples below. Then cut the strips apart and pass them to classmates or friends. Ask each one to write a beginning that leads to the ending on the strip.

a poem about an escaped wild animal

a letter to an editor expressing a complaint about something

a surprising or funny event that happened at school

a news report about an accident or fire

an explanation of how to get your homework done on time

a warning about an unhealthy or dangerous activity

a report of a mysterious disappearance

a lesson on making a good milkshake

Use with page 24.

Name

LOST HEADLINES

These news stories Murphy has prepared for the magazines have lost their headlines. Read each one. Then add a good, short headline. Remember that a headline must give readers a good idea about what will be in the story or report.

Spark Magazine — Page 1

An unusual rash of spider bites has been reported in the county this month. Officials are puzzled by the statistics. In the past four weeks, 127 bites by scorpions and other spiders have been reported. Most of the bites have occurred in the homes of the victims. Local scientists are trying to determine if there is an increase in the number of spiders in the area.

Spark Magazine — Page 2

Schools throughout the city were closed at noon yesterday. School officials would give no reason for the closure, except to insist that it was necessary. Students and parents have been guessing about the reasons. Some believe that the water supply at one of the schools was contaminated.

Spark Magazine — Page 3

People in cities and towns along the coast are suffering from attacks by killer bees. Thousands of animals and people have been stung by the bees. The stings produce strong flu-like symptoms. Hundreds of people have become critically ill, and 45 animals have died.

Spark Magazine — Page 4

A local librarian is enjoying her good luck today because she is $132,000 richer than she was yesterday. Mrs. Leslie Anne Ruddenbacher, assistant librarian at the Ames County Library, found a $100 bill stuck in every page of a recently returned book. The person who last borrowed the book said that the money did not belong to her.

Spark Magazine — Page 5

The Lynwood–Crater football game was a thriller down to the final seconds. Lynwood controlled the ball and led by 1 point with 15 seconds left. Then the Crater defense got to the quarterback and brought him down behind the goal line, giving Crater 2 points for a safety. This is the seventeenth win in a row for the Crater Comets. Their win broke a seven-game winning streak for the Lynwood Lions.

Spark Magazine — Page 6

Citizens of Millerstown are staying indoors this week. An eight-year-old lion escaped from a circus train as the train passed through the town last Monday. The train was making a brief stop for supplies when a conductor noticed the gate on the lion's cage was broken. Searchers are combing the area. Anyone catching sight of the lion should not approach the animal, but should call the Miller County Police.

Use with page 27.

Name

Add a good, short headline for each news story.

Spark Magazine

Page 7

Six high school skiers won medals at the state ski meet this weekend. Jonathan Mogul, a freshman, took first place in the slalom. Tom Turner, also a freshman, finished second. Tina Vann set a new state record with a win in the downhill. Her teammates Anna Georges and Teresa Gomez took second and third. Jana Jensen won gold in the freestyle event.

Spark Magazine **Page 8**

A strange robbery took place Saturday night at the local sandwich shop—or did it? Juan Mirana, owner of Subs to Go, found twenty long loaves of wheat bread, a box of onions, and two large jars of pickles missing from his shop on Sunday morning. There was no sign of a break-in, however, and the doors were still locked when he arrived.

Spark Magazine

Page 9

Police reported a sharp increase in traffic tickets in Millerstown this year. Parking tickets inside city limits increased by fifty percent. The number of speeding tickets jumped from 25 last year to 380 this year. Tickets for reckless driving have doubled in the last year. It is not clear whether these increases are caused by more careless drivers, or by better police work.

Spark Magazine **Page 10**

Five hundred people attended a unique wedding last Saturday at the Jeston Chapel. Three couples were married in a triple ceremony. The three brides are triplets Molly, Polly, and Lolly Bridges. Each bride had a maid of honor, a flower girl, and three bridesmaids. There were three ministers in charge of the ceremony, Rev. Starks, Rev. Sparks, and Rev. Marks. The couples had a triple reception following the ceremony.

Spark Magazine

Page 11

A busload of tourists claims to have seen Bigfoot on Sunday. The tour bus was headed south on I-5 near Salem, Oregon, when a large creature appeared out of the woods. All 43 passengers on the bus testified to seeing the creature.

Spark Magazine **Page 12**

A record-setting pumpkin was grown in Dade County this fall. Farmer Butch Appleby's prize pumpkin weighed 980 pounds. After officials decided it was the heaviest pumpkin grown in the county, Farmer Butch got out his chainsaw and turned the pumpkin into a fantastic Jack-O-Lantern.

Use with page 26.

Name

GREAT CHOICES

"Looking for a great place to visit on your next vacation?" Murphy has a good start on her travel column for next week's magazine, but her article needs details added to tell about each place. Choose three strong supporting details to support her main statement for each paragraph. Use the ideas in the box below, or write your own.

Catch a glimpse of a mirage.
Enjoy cool drinks in a green oasis.
The sun will shine until midnight!
Enjoy some unusually fine fishing.
Get some close-up photos of big crocodiles.
Climb on glaciers and photograph icebergs.
Find out what it's really like to ride on a camel.

Spend a whole day watching playful penguins.
See for yourself the most mammoth ice shelf in the world.
See some of the most beautiful tropical birds in the world.
You might catch a glimpse of a cheetah or an anaconda.
Find plants and animals that survive on very little water.
Watch the wind create dunes and patterns in the sand.
Experience a lush tropical rain forest first hand.

Do you have a vacation coming up? Would you like to visit an exciting, unusual spot?
Call your travel agent today, and make your next trip one you won't forget!

Stock up on sunscreen and head for the Great Sahara Desert.

_____

_____

_____

Grab your mosquito netting and your camera for an adventure on the great, wide Amazon River.

_____

_____

_____

If you don't mind getting a bit cold, try the adventure of a lifetime in frosty Antarctica!

_____

_____

_____

Name _____

28

TERRIBLE CHOICES

Butterfly hunting in Quick-Sand Swamp is probably a "no-no."

Maybe Murphy should expand her travel column and warn readers about places not to visit! Get her started on this feature for the next SPARK edition.

Complete the outline to get started on your column. For each main section of the outline, write a topic sentence describing a place to avoid. Then write three or more supporting sentences giving details about why everyone should stay away from that place.

TERRIBLE CHOICES FOR YOUR VACATION
I strongly recommend that you stay far away from these places on your next vacation. Believe me, I know about these spots. I barely survived them myself!

I. _____
   A. _____
   B. _____
   C. _____

II. _____
   A. _____
   B. _____
   C. _____

III. _____
   A. _____
   B. _____
   C. _____

IV. _____
   A. _____
   B. _____
   C. _____

Use with page 28.

Name

COURTROOM IMPOSTORS

What confusion happened today in the Miller County Court! Five people, all claiming to be Pat Pagoo, showed up to claim a large sum of money left by a wealthy relative. How will the judge ever figure out who the four impostors are?

Read the court reports below. Each report on these two pages (30 and 31) has one or more details that are not related to the report. These details have slipped into the writing, but do not belong. Track down any details that are not helpful to the article's purpose, and cross out these "impostors"!

Thursday, February 19, 1998

CASE #1

Five people showed up in Judge Law's courtroom today. All of them claimed to be Pat Pagoo, heir to a twenty-million-dollar fortune. Judge Law had just had a turkey club sandwich for lunch when the case began. All five Pat Pagoos brought birth certificates to prove their identity. Judge Law coughed from a bad cold. Then Judge Law postponed the case until authorities could investigate the background of the people and determine which ones were impostors.

Will the real Pat Pagoo please stand up?

CASE #2

Mr. Pilfer pled "not guilty."

Daphne Hart brought a complaint against Anthony Pilfer. Anthony was wearing a suit and tie in court today. Daphne claimed that Anthony left her candy shop on Valentine's Day without paying for some chocolates. Miss Hart told the judge that Mr. Pilfer had a 20-pound box of chocolates under his raincoat when he slipped out the back door of the shop. Mr. Pilfer pled "not guilty" and reported that he is allergic to chocolate.

CASE #3

Mrs. Grundy lives in a pink house on Blossom Street. She told the judge that her grandchildren visit her every Saturday. She is suing her next door neighbors, the Jeffersons. She wants them to pay $400 for the tulip bulbs and daffodil bulbs that their dog dug up from her garden. The Jeffersons claimed that they do not have a dog. Mrs. Grundy has a cat. The judge found that a dog named Tulip is registered under this family's name. He ordered the Jeffersons to pay Mrs. Grundy $400.

Mrs. Grundy swore to tell the truth.

Use with page 31.

Name

Cross out the details that are not helpful to purpose of the writing.

Cream puff fakery?

CASE #4

The Cream Puff Heaven Bakery was brought into court today and charged with false advertising. Mr. Charles E. Claire buys four cream puffs every day from the bakery. He also buys a dozen sticky buns and two pumpkin pies. According to Mr. Claire, the bakery is using artificial whipped cream in its puffs. He brought in the bakery's newspaper ad, which claims that genuine whipped cream is used in all their pastries. The judge ordered the bakery owner to bring him a dozen cream puffs to sample, so that he can decide if the cream is fake.

CASE #5

Judge Laws heard the case of Arthur Rush next. Arthur Rush makes his living designing socks for the Shoes & Socks Emporium. Mr. Rush received four speeding tickets in one week. Mr. Rush drives a Mustang and Judge Laws drives a Volkswagen. The judge ordered Mr. Rush to pay all fines and to attend Speeder's School for eight weeks.

"Pay the fine," ordered the Judge.

A problem tree.

CASE #6

Agatha Abernathy is suing the city of Millerstown. The city has ordered Mrs. Abernathy to cut down a diseased tree in front of her house. The city has a population of 21,000. Her house has three stories. The city claims the tree will cause a hazard when it dies. She claims the tree belongs to the city because its roots are under the street, which is city property. The judge agreed with Mrs. Abernathy and ordered the city to remove the tree.

Write a court report for the last case of the day. Include one or more details that do not belong. Ask a friend or classmate to search your report for the "impostors." Draw a picture to go along with your report.

CASE #7

_____

_____

_____

_____

_____

Use with page 30.

Name

QUITE BY ACCIDENT

Murphy was in such a hurry to get this accident report written that she got it all mixed up. Can you straighten it out before it goes to press?

When I arrived, I found Farmer McCully's pigs looking shocked. No one was hurt, not even the pigs. Farmer McCully called 911 at noon to report a loud roaring sound that was shaking the earth near his farm. Just then, I heard terrible screaming in addition to the loud roaring sound. Unbelievably, a bathtub was whirling through the air. I was in the area, so I raced to the farm. I looked up in the sky toward the terrible noise. Fortunately, the tub landed safely in the pig pen. A young man in the tub was screaming for his life.

Write the sentences in a better sequence, so that the report makes sense and is interesting to the readers.

_____

_____

_____

_____

_____

_____

_____

_____

_____

_____

Name

UNSOLVED MYSTERIES

SPARK magazine has received some entries for "The Mystery Corner." Every one of them has sentence trouble! The sentences are all short and choppy. Writing is more interesting if the length and structure of the sentences vary.

Rewrite each of these mysteries. Combine or rearrange the sentences so that they form a smooth-flowing paragraph with a variety of sentence lengths. Use a separate piece of paper to rewrite the mysteries.

The Case of the Missing Pizzas
At noon it was discovered.
Thirteen pizzas were missing from Papa Gino's.
Size 10 footprints were found at the scene.
Three suspects were caught.
Bart had pizza sauce on his shirt.
Burt had cheese shreds in his hair.
Brett had a guilty smirk on his face.
Burt wears size 12 shoes.
Bart slept until noon.
Brett wears size 8 shoes.
Police solved the mystery.
They arrested one of the suspects.
Who stole the pizzas?

The Great Escape
The room has one door.
The door is locked.
It cannot be unlocked from inside.
The room has no windows.
The room has a cracked skylight.
There is a ladder in the room.
The man in the room has no tools.
At midnight it was raining.
By 2:00 P.M., the temperature was below freezing.
The cat slept on the outside step.
The cat has not been disturbed.
The man is not in the room.
How did he escape?

A Crash in the Night
The night is dark.
Long shadows lurk in every corner.
The streets are empty.
Only a lone streetlight lights a corner.
Heavy mist hangs in the air.
There is not a sound.
Nothing is moving.
Suddenly, a crash splits the silence.
Shattered glass sprinkles to the ground.
Then it is quiet again.
What caused the crash?

Name

OLD NEWS IS NEW NEWS

Murphy turns an old story into today's news by changing the form of writing. A Mother Goose nursery rhyme becomes a news article! She also writes the story of Jack Sprat and his wife in some other forms.

COUPLE SUFFERS STRANGE DISEASE

City Center Hospital admitted a man and his wife today. Each suffers from a rare eating disorder. The man, Mr. Jack Sprat, of 1616 Hambone Lane, has a condition that makes it impossible for him to eat anything but meat. His wife, Maryanne Sprat, of the same address, says she can eat nothing but fat. Both of them are being tested by medical experts who are looking for the cause of their ailments. Doctors are puzzled about how to treat the couple. Mr. Sprat had a positive outlook. "One good thing," he said, "no food is wasted in our household!"

WANT AD

WANTED:

Man that can eat no fat seeks girlfriend who eats no meat. Call 555-0001 after 3 P.M.

LIMERICK

There once was a young man named Sprat
Whose wife could eat only fat
But one day he found
That she craved some ground round
And it started a horrible spat!

LETTER

Dear Maryanne,
I cannot take it any more! Night after night I sit with my boring, lean chicken or steak and watch while you delight with your French fries and cream puffs, fudgy ice cream and rich gravy. I have to confess that I crave those rich, fatty foods you eat. I must try them. I beg you, please trade places with me for just one night!
Your loving, starving husband,
Jack

Jack Sprat could eat no fat.
His wife could eat no lean.
And so between the two of them,
They licked the platter clean!

ODE

Ode to a Burger
Oh, how I'd love to taste you
Once...If only I could
You know that I would!
I'd love to savor
Your charcoal flavor
To slurp those juices you've got...
But, alas, I cannot!

TONGUE TWISTER

Two twins with tricky tastes never tasted two tastes.

Use with page 35.

Name

Start with a well-known tale or story. Write it in four different forms. Choose one of the tales listed, or another one you know. Write a limerick, news article, letter, thank-you note, recipe, poem, ad, menu, announcement, song, tall tale, bumper sticker, speech, or poster based on the story.

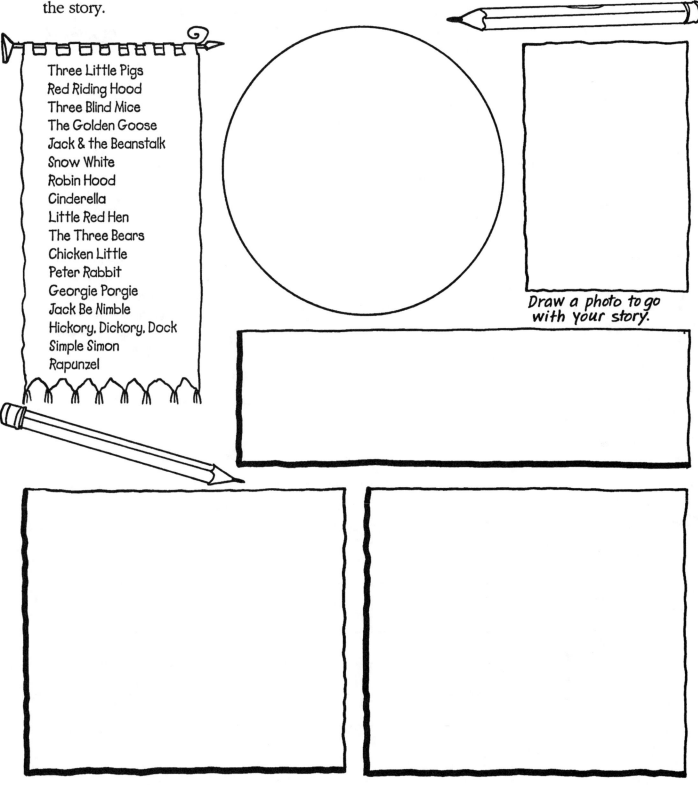

Three Little Pigs
Red Riding Hood
Three Blind Mice
The Golden Goose
Jack & the Beanstalk
Snow White
Robin Hood
Cinderella
Little Red Hen
The Three Bears
Chicken Little
Peter Rabbit
Georgie Porgie
Jack Be Nimble
Hickory, Dickory, Dock
Simple Simon
Rapunzel

Draw a photo to go with your story.

Use with page 34.

Name

STRANGE DISAPPEARANCES

Science cannot explain the shocking weekend news from southern Florida. Murphy made this scientific mystery the subject of her Science Curiosities column in last week's edition of SPARK magazine.

MISSING IN THE ATLANTIC

by Murphy Green

Four strange disappearances were reported to the Coast Guard in Miami last weekend. On Friday at noon, the Quick family headed east into the Atlantic Ocean for an afternoon sailing trip on their new 20-foot catamaran. They did not return.

Several hours later, SunAir Flight 23 from Puerto Rico disappeared into the clouds over Miami and never came out.

On Saturday, two fishing boats in the same area did not come back to the harbor at the end of the day.

A fourth disappearance was reported on Sunday. A Miami woman and her husband were parasailing off the coast of Bermuda. Relatives watched them disappeared into a wall of mist. They have not been seen since.

Searchers have been covering the area for days. So far, they have found no trace of any of the missing boats, persons, or aircraft. Scientists are not able to explain the cause of many strange disappearances that have been reported in this area known as "The Bermuda Triangle."

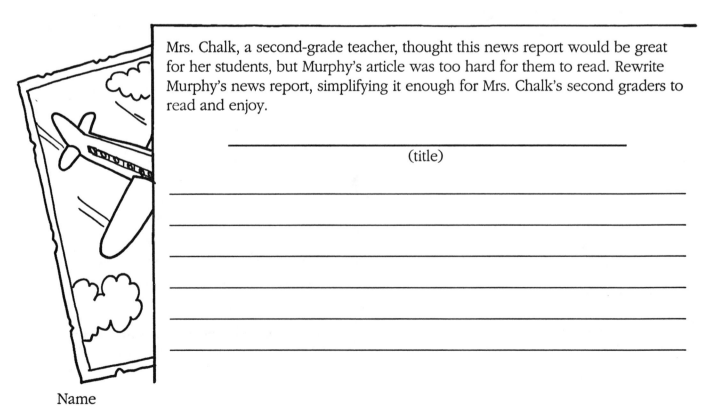

Mrs. Chalk, a second-grade teacher, thought this news report would be great for her students, but Murphy's article was too hard for them to read. Rewrite Murphy's news report, simplifying it enough for Mrs. Chalk's second graders to read and enjoy.

_____

(title)

_____

_____

_____

_____

_____

_____

Name

COMING ALIVE!

This week's Literature Page features examples of a tool used often in literature by writers who want their writing to be interesting. This tool or "literary technique" is called **personification.** When writers use personification, they give characteristics of living things to objects that are **not** alive.

My toaster is a sizzling, hungry monster.
It swallows my toast into its fiery jaws,
And hands it back to me, all crumbly and black.
Jennifer Gray, Gr. 4

I am a pot with a black handle,
People pour water in and out.
"Stop! Stop! My belly is on fire!" I yell.
"My belly my belly, it's on fire!"
"Help me!"
Elizabeth Psomas, Gr. 4

The river sings a lazy bubbling tune to me.
The notes are low and soft, and her voice is like a lullaby.
Angela DiGorgo, Gr. 5

In the desert
A massive bridge of rock
Rises against the sky
Gazing up at snow-capped
Mountains.
Nelson Kling, Gr. 5

The wind licks at my chapped face.
The wind plays games with my umbrella.
She tickles my eyelashes,
and whispers silly sayings into my ears.
Jordan Jameson, Gr. 5

Write a line or a short poem about 4 of these objects. Use personification to give characteristics of a person or other living thing to each of the objects.

numbers on a math test	a mirror	my mailbox	spaghetti	my cereal
snow, hail, or rain	the sun	a blender	a lemon drop	the fog
an ocean wave	candles	the shower	my gym shoes	my pillow
an ice cream sundae	my umbrella	a headache	the sidewalk	a skateboard

Name _____

SPEAKING IN METAPHORS

The For Kids Only page is full of metaphors! What is a metaphor? It is a comparison between two things that are not alike. If a comparison uses the word *like* or the word *as,* then it is called a simile. It is such fun to create metaphors and similes, especially when you try to compare things that are very different!

SPARK MAGAZINE

FOR KIDS

ONLY

Losing a friend is like peanut butter and jelly apart.
Kayla Bryant

*Falling through space is like
going to school on Monday. (It never ends!)*
Simone Wren

MATH IS A HURRICANE OF NUMBERS.
Ariana Lewis

A kid in class looking at the clock
is like a crocodile lurking in the swamp.
Looking for his dinner,
very sneaky, very sly,
he catches every meal he spies.
Greg Cross

*When my little brother is angry,
It's like a raging tornado
going through the house.*
Matthew Bianca

**Writing a new story
is like creating a new world.**
Matthew Bianca

*The scratching of a pencil
is like the scurry of a mouse.*
Tessah Joseph

*Life is like a dark pool of water—
you never know what's in it.*
Laura Arndt

**I am the universe
The sun burning with rage
The planets dusty and lifeless
The stars hot but blue
I am the galaxy
I am.......**
Jamie Cross

**Math problems are like
hot, boring days that never end.**
Rachael Wanderscheid

Poets are like the wind.
Simone Wren

Life is like a gift waiting to be opened.
Camille Morris

Life is like an everlasting gobstopper.
Camille Morris

Write a comparison for each thing listed on page 39.
Use with page 39.

Name

Finish the comparisons.

1. Life is like _____.

2. School is as _____ as _____.

3. The kids in my class sound like _____.

4. Writing a poem is like _____.

5. Music is _____.

6. Math problems are like _____.

7. Eating potato chips is like _____.

8. This music is as loud as _____.

9. When _____ is angry, it's like _____.

10. Morning is as _____ as _____.

11. I am like _____.

12. My temper is as _____ as _____.

13. The winter was like _____.

14. Losing a friend is like _____.

15. _____ is like _____.

16. Being in the dark is as _____ as _____.

17. Getting your feelings hurt is like _____.

18. Getting stung by a bee is like _____.

19. Moving is like _____.

20. Sisters (or brothers) are like _____.

21. _____ is like _____.

22. _____ is a _____.

Use with page 38.

Name

NO BONES ABOUT IT!

Dear Reader, Don't be a couch potato!

Dr. Payne Free

SPARK magazine has just added a Health & Fitness page. This page features questions from readers looking for advice from Dr. Payne Free about taking care of their health!

Dr. Free's readers use lots of figurative language in their letters. Figurative language is the use of a word or words to mean something different from the literal or usual meaning. Circle the examples of figurative language used in the letters to and from Dr. Free.

- That's a pretty pickle!
- raining cats and dogs
- drive me up a wall
- I can see right through you.
- go out on a limb
- a bone to pick with you
- You spilled the beans.
- not worth a hill of beans
- a frog in my throat
- Don't jump the gun.
- lost her head
- gone bananas
- I'm tickled pink!
- lost her cool
- My car's a real lemon!
- ham it up
- Get out of my hair!
- a backseat driver
- She's pretty burned up.
- tongue tied
- got her nose in a book
- cook your goose
- the last straw
- Keep a lid on it!

Use with page 41.

Name

Dear Dr. Free,
My wife says I'm making too many bones about this topic, but I must ask you about a problem. I've had a frog in my throat for two months. It began one March night when it was raining cats and dogs, and I'm pretty burned up about not being able to get rid of it. I am about to go off my rocker. Can you help me?

Sincerely,
Robert Lozenge

Dear Robert,
You are not barking up the wrong tree! I agree that you're up a creek, for sure! Take four doses of my special defrogging liquid, and you'll be in the pink before long!

Sincerely,
Dr. Free

Dear Dr. Free,
I have been tongue-tied for a long time about my problem, but I'll stick my neck out and ask you. I have been exercising my head off now for six months. Every time I go out for a jog, my ears grow longer. I am not pulling your leg! I am very down in the dumps about this. Should I quit jogging?

Sincerely,
Veronica Lobes

Dear Veronica,
Well, I'll be a monkey's uncle! This takes the cake! This blows my mind! I am stumped! This must be driving you up a wall! Get yourself to the hospital, quick as a wink, for some tests. Let me know what they find!

Sincerely,
Dr. Free

Dear Dr. Free,
I need some facts straight from the horse's mouth! I am fit to be tied. My nose bleeds from sunup to sundown. My father had the same problem. I guess I'm just a chip off the old block! What do you recommend?

Sincerely,
Sam Troubled

Dear Sam,
You should be crying your eyes out, man! I'm going to pass the buck on this one and send you to a blood clinic. I also suggest that if you get near any vampires, you scream your head off and burn rubber getting out of there! Good luck!

Sincerely,
Dr. Free

Now, write a letter of your own to Dr. Free. Also write Dr. Free's answer. Use as many examples of figurative language as you can!

Dear Dr. Payne Free,

Dear _____,

- Don't let her get your goat!
- fit to be tied
- straight from the horse's mouth
- He's a bad apple.
- pass the buck
- eat humble pie
- dressed to the nines
- cat's got her tongue
- up a creek
- in hot water
- shaking in my boots
- He'll bite my head off!
- a red-letter day
- blow her top
- go off his rocker
- lost his marbles
- take the cake
- screaming bloody murder!
- quick as a wink
- Make no bones about it.
- pull the wool over your eyes
- in the doghouse
- let the cat out of the bag
- crying your eyes out
- down in the dumps
- madder than a wet hen

Use with page 40.

Name

HE SAID...SHE SAID

The cartoonist is hard at work getting ready for the next edition of SPARK magazine. In her cartoons, she uses "talk balloons" to show what the characters are saying. When you write about a conversation, you must include dialogue in the paragraphs.

For each conversation in the cartoon, write a paragraph that includes the dialogue. Make sure you use quotation marks and other punctuation marks correctly. Use another sheet of paper.

Name

IN THE MOOD

There's screaming! There's excitement! The crowd is wild! Charlie's assignment tonight is to write a story about the high school championship football game. Everyone in town will want to read about this. He needs to choose the right words and phrases to let readers know what it is like to be at the game.

Charlie chose the phrases below to set the mood. Add three (or more) words or phrases to help Charlie.

crashing of helmets
roaring crowd   wild cheers
screeching, screaming
wild excitement
sweet, sticky cotton candy
salty, greasy, yummy popcorn
speeding runners   crisp, fall air
inviting smell of steamy hot dogs and strong coffee
arms waving and fans jumping
cartwheels and flips of cheerleaders
nonstop celebration and backslapping
laughter, moans, groans, squeals

Your assignment is to write about the topics below. How will you set the mood? Write several words and phrases that will set a particular mood for each one. You may also write an opening line to set the mood.

A mystery	**A poem about a tornado**	**A description of a soft snowfall**

Name

HERE'S HOW

Once every month, SPARK magazine includes a How To Do It page. Readers submit written explanations of how to do something they think is important. It is Murphy's job to choose the entries and polish them up for publishing. She likes this one, but it is missing all its connections! Choose some connecting words or phrases to fill in the blanks in this article.

first

second

then

at last

because

at the same time

in addition

to begin with

next

soon

later

meanwhile

after a while

finally

much later

when that is done

for example

THE WORLD'S BEST MILKSHAKE
How to Make It!

_____, you must buy the best, tastiest, creamiest, richest vanilla ice cream you can find. _____, it is necessary to have rich, whole milk. _____, if you don't have whole milk, you could use low-fat milk. _____, have vanilla, fresh strawberries, powdered malt, and whipped cream on hand. Start by getting the strawberries ready. Strawberries are often dirty and gritty when you buy them._____, you'll need to wash them well. _____fill your blender 1/3 full with them. Sprinkle them with a teaspoon of sugar. _____, fill the blender up to ¾ full with ice cream. Pour in about 1 cup of milk. _____, sprinkle 2 tablespoons of malt powder on the top. Run the blender on medium speed until the shake is mixed well. _____, get the whipped cream and one perfect whole strawberry ready. Pour the shake into a tall glass, and top it with whipped cream and the strawberry. _____of your careful efforts, you will have a delicious shake! Enjoy!

for instance

therefore

as a result

however

much later

when that is done

for example

for instance

therefore

as a result

however

on the other hand

instead

because of this

also

in spite of this

Now that you have had a little practice with connections, write a how-to article of your own. Explain how do to something. Some of the ideas below might interest you, but you can also use something else! Write your explanation on a separate piece of paper.

HOW TO . . .

ride a snowboard	pass a test	catch a lizard	build a good fort	wash a dog	avoid the flu
write a poem	wrestle an alligator	get gum out of hair	feed a lion	climb a glacier	eat a taco
clean your room	do a somersault	make a pizza	make lasagna	change kitty litter	get rid of a cold

Name

THE TALLEST OF TALES

FROSTBITE in MONTANA

How cold is cold? Do you think you have ever really been cold? Well, listen to this, and then you can decide. Last winter I went to Montana to visit my Uncle Fred. He told me to bring warm clothes. Was I ever glad that I did. The first morning that I was there, it was so cold that the chickens laid frozen eggs and the cows gave ice cream instead of milk. My words froze as I spoke them and dropped right to the ground and shattered. The dog's shadow froze on the ground the minute he stepped out of the house. Uncle Fred said that shadow did not thaw until April. Well, that's the last time I'll visit Montana in the winter. Uncle Fred says to come in August. He wants me to see the chicken lay scrambled eggs from the terrible heat.

WANTED: The tallest tale in the county!

It's time for the Tall Tale Contest again. SPARK magazine is waiting for its readers to send in tall tales this year.

REQUIREMENTS: The tale **must** have facts or details that show great exaggeration. These must be things that could not possibly be true! This is one place where lies are okay! In fact, the bigger the lies, the better the tale!

Would you like to enter the contest? Choose a topic that is a good one for exaggeration. Then write a tale and polish it until it is ready to send in to the magazine. Make sure your tale has: a good title
a smashing beginning
a solid middle
a great ending
Good luck! Maybe you'll win a tall, tall prize!

Start your Tall Tale here:

_____
_____
_____
_____
_____
_____
_____
_____
_____
_____
_____
_____
_____
_____
_____
_____
_____
_____
_____

Name

CLIFF-HANGERS

Everybody loves a cliff-hanger! It's a tale that leads you to an exciting, breathtaking, mysterious, or dangerous point—and leaves you hanging! You don't know what happens next. Charlie loves cliff-hangers. He loves to write them, and he loves to finish them. Finish Charlie's cliff-hanger and give it a title. Use a separate sheet of paper.

> Joe knew it was not a good idea to be in the school at night. He would never have gone there, if it weren't for that math test tomorrow. He just had to have the math book he had left in his locker. Otherwise, he would fail the test. He had hoped to find a janitor working at the school, but there was no one there. Surprisingly, the door from the parking lot was unlocked. "I'll just run in, grab my book, and race right back out!" he told his mom. He flipped on the hall light and hurried to his locker. His hands shook as he tried the combination. He had to do it twice. Just as he got the math book and slammed his locker shut, the light went out. He heard no sounds. Everything was black! Quickly, he headed back down the hall to the door and pushed against it. To his shock, the door was locked. He could not get out! "It's a good thing Mom is waiting just outside the door in the car!" he said to himself. "She'll see me and get help." When he looked out the window, the parking lot was empty!

Next, write the beginning to your own cliff-hanger. Include something surprising, mysterious, or unusual to catch the interest of your reader. (See the Idea List.) Then, trade cliff-hangers with your friends. Finish each other's tales to tell what happened next!

Idea List
an accident
an unexpected visitor
a secret
a dream that isn't a dream
a missing friend
a strange shadow
caught on the train track
the trunk in the attic
the forbidden cave
a flash flood
a mysterious building
an unusual code
the scary computer

Name _____

CONVINCE ME!

Murphy's jingle has been a great success! Since it was first placed in the magazine three months ago, the sales of MBG (Mystery Bubble Gum) have tripled! Now, many companies want her to convince people to buy their products. Give her some help. Write a jingle (the text), a catchy slogan, an ad, or a short argument that will convince buyers to try these products.

MBG is the bubblegum for me
I don't care if it's got broccoli!

Carrots, peas, and berries
Onions, beans, and cherries
It's got fruits galore
And veggies twenty-four.

We buy packs by the dozen.
I share them with my cousin.
I love to chew and pop it.
No vitamin can stop it.

I don't care if it's got broccoli
'Cause MBG is the bubblegum for me!

Write a paragraph, poem, advertisement, or song that could convince someone to **do** one of these things. (Or you may choose something else!)

   ... try eating chocolate-covered ants
   ... learn to use the Internet
   ... take a trip to the Bermuda Triangle
   ... buy organic food
   ... learn to ride a wild bull
   ... never get a tattoo
   ... search for Bigfoot in a deep forest
   ... ride an upside-down roller coaster
   ... go to summer school

tuna-artichoke ice cream

a parrot hat

try eating chocolate-covered ants

Name _____

WHAT CHARACTERS!

SPARK magazine held a contest for their Believe It or Not column. The magazine wanted to feature stories about people who had done unusual and unbelievable things. They printed an ad inviting people with special talents or accomplishments to come to the magazine office for interviews. To write about these interesting characters, the reporters need to collect some good words for describing people. The words on pages 48 and 49 are examples of good words for writing about characters.

For each character on these two pages, write a list of interesting words that you might use to describe her or him.

peppy
suspicious
athletic
outrageous
adventurous
quirky
elderly
eccentric
limber
offensive
arrogant
courageous
sleazy
droopy
cheerful
rotund
musical
insomniac
fearless
annoying
dependable
hilarious
clever
serious
stubborn
mature
precocious
massive
patient

1. owner of the world's smallest pony

2. person who's gone the longest time without sleep

3. holds the world paddleball-bounce record

4. the oldest skydiver in the country

Use with page 49.

Name

comical
lazy
mean
humble
delightful
unpredictable
forgetful
wicked
energetic
miserable
watchful
talented
creative
old-fashioned
persistent
foolish
rebellious
reasonable
unreasonable
attractive
joyous
sparkling
gloomy
mischievous
mysterious
lonely
reclusive
jolly

Create a name for each of the characters on pages 48 and 49.

1. _____   5. _____

2. _____   6. _____

3. _____   7. _____

4. _____   8. _____

Write a list of interesting words that you might use to describe each character. Then choose one of the eight characters and write at least one paragraph describing that character. Use another sheet of paper.

5. owns a potato shaped like Abraham Lincoln.

6. inventor of a machine that translates animal language

7. claims to be Elvis Presley

8. person who walks only on his hands

Use with page 48.

Name

PICTURE THIS

Sam takes photographs to match many of the stories and articles written by the reporters. For the upcoming edition of SPARK magazine, some of the pictures were lost. Some of the writing was lost, too! On these two pages (pages 50 and 51), replace the missing writing and photographs.

If the writing is missing, write a story, article, advertisement, poem, joke, essay, opinion, letter, or other feature to match the visual story presented by the picture. If the photo is missing, draw a picture that illustrates the article.

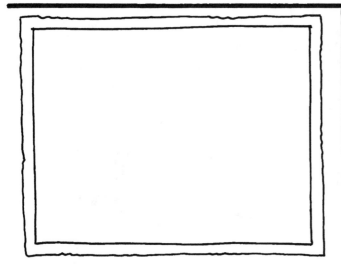

1.

Sharks have come to our beaches! Lifeguards and swimmers have reported many sightings of sharks close to shore at the beaches south of the city. One surfer reported a very close call. A shark actually took a huge bite out of his board! Sharks rarely come into the swimming area or bother swimmers. Officials have closed the beaches to swimmers until further notice—and until the sharks move on to deeper waters!

Use with page 51.

2.

_____

_____

_____

_____

_____

_____

_____

_____

_____

_____

_____

Name

PICTURE THIS, CONT.

If the writing is missing, write a story, article, advertisement, or other feature to match the picture. If the photo is missing, draw a picture that illustrates the article.

3. Another tightrope walker attempts to cross the Grand Canyon. Tomasina M. Balance took her first steps at noon on Thursday in what was the first attempt to cross the canyon in years. She balanced for forty-five minutes before breathless crowds on both sides of the canyon. Much to the relief of everyone, she successfully completed the walk!

4. The mayor gave away a key to the city today to a special guest. Centerville was visited by Pierre the Giant, a well-known actor who is over eight feet tall and weighs 450 pounds. Pierre was born in Centerville, but he has not visited the city since he was in first grade. It was quite a sight to see him stand beside Mayor Cathy Graham, who is only 5 feet 1 inch tall in her high heels!

5. _____
_____
_____
_____
_____
_____
_____
_____
_____
_____
_____

Use with page 50.

Name

IN MY OPINION

Letters to the editor are strictly opinion. Many people write to the editor of SPARK magazine. They might comment on something that the magazine published, or their comments might be about anything at all. Read these letters to the editor. They need some editing! Correct the spelling, punctuation, and capitalization. Cross out any unnecessary ideas. If any ideas are out of order, draw arrows to rearrange them. Make any other changes that will improve the writing.

Dear Editor:
Why are you saying negative things in yur magazine about the new city tax on food in all the restrants. What is your problom? The tax is for a good cauzze. just a small amount on each meal adds up to thousands of dollers for our parks. This is really good for kids. it gives us a wunderful swiming pool, too. This is a small price to pay for so much good stuf the cost is really pretty small And our restrants have good food. If I by a $4.00 sandwich, it only costs 20 extra for the tax. even if someone gets a very expenzave meal—say $50.00, the 5% tax stil only adds $2.50. That's not bad! It gives us nice, cleen places to play socer and softball.

Sincerely,
Whitney

Dear Editor,
In you're September ishue you had a great artickle about pushy snowboarders. I tuv winter sports I think boarders shud be banned from the mountain.

Dear Editor,
Your article about snow-boarders was terrible and untrue. Why are you picking on snow boarders? They're citizens, too. Why don't you get off their backs? they're

signed,
Disgruntled

Dear Editor
No one has asked the kids! everywon in the town is talking about year-round school. All the adults keep haveing heerings and meatings to discuss this. some committee is making a plan for school to go thrugh the summer. I am really mad! I am on a dance team. if something is being planned that changes our whole lives, expecially takeing away our summers, it is unfair to go ahead without taking to the students. we have opinions, too we should be the ones to decide this, since it is all about our education.

Sincerely,
Madder Than A Wet Hen

Use with page 53.

Name

IN MY OPINION, CONT.

Write some of your opinions in letters to the editor. Write an opinion about two of the topics suggested, or choose topics of your own. Make sure your personal belief about the topic shows in your writing. Your letter should also include reasons or arguments to support your opinion.

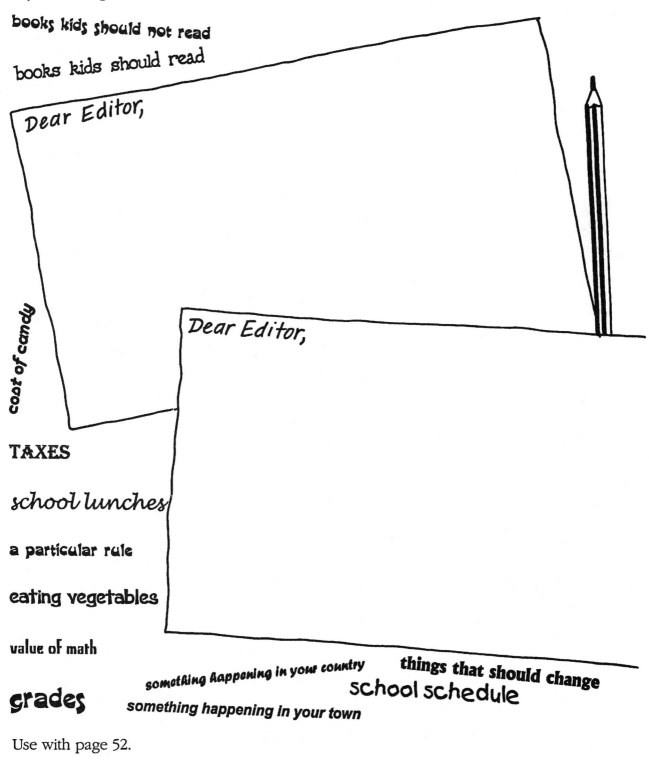

books kids should not read

books kids should read

Dear Editor,

cost of candy

TAXES

school lunches

a particular rule

eating vegetables

value of math

grades

Dear Editor,

something happening in your country   **things that should change**

school schedule

something happening in your town

Use with page 52.

Name

THE RED PAGE

In celebration of Valentine's Day, Charlie and the new graphic artist are putting together a *Red Page* for the magazine. It will have poems about *red*. Think about *red* things so that you can send something to Charlie! Pay attention to all five senses. Collect ideas about things that look, smell, sound, taste, and feel *red*. Write down *red* places and experiences. Use your ideas to finish the *red* poem below.

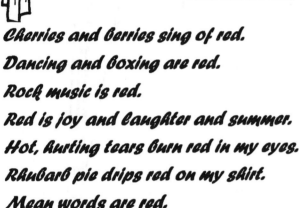

RED

Red burns across embarrassed cheeks.
Ramon Tomel, Gr. 4

Cherries and berries sing of red.
Dancing and boxing are red.
Rock music is red.
Red is joy and laughter and summer.
Hot, hurting tears burn red in my eyes.
Rhubarb pie drips red on my shirt.
Mean words are red.
Alyssa Meyers, Gr. 5

Red is a bloody nose and anger.
Red is candy hearts and roses.
Red is a cherry pie baking,
And the smell of homemade spaghetti sauce.
I feel red when someone makes fun of me.
A cold nose feels red. So does July.
Sirens scream red, and newborn babies cry red.
Red is an argument with my brother.
Hot peppers on my tongue burn red.
Jason Williams, Gr. 5

Red is _____, _____, and _____.

_____ is red. So is _____.

_____ and _____ sound red.

Red is the taste of _____ and _____.

_____ feels red.

My favorite red place is _____.

_____ sounds red.

Red is _____, and red is _____.

I feel red when _____.

So is _____.

Try some *green, yellow, orange, red, black,* or *blue* writing, too!

Name _____

APPENDIX

CONTENTS

THE WRITING PROCESS

Stage 1 — Getting a Great Idea and Getting Excited
. . . a group experience; an individual experience; a piece of literature; an unexpected happening; a common feeling; a question; a memory; a discussion; a surprise happening; an activity in any content area—*anything that sparks your writing!*

Stage 2 — Collecting Impressions
. . . the gathering of ideas, words, fragments, thoughts, facts, phrases, questions, and observations . . . the process of brainstorming about and getting ready to tell about your main idea

Stage 3 — Organizing
. . . the time for taking a close look at all those words, phrases, and ideas you have collected and thinking about what fits together . . . this is the time for asking yourself questions such as . . . *What goes with this idea? Which ideas should be grouped together? Where would this fit into the whole picture? What do these ideas or phrases have in common?*

Stage 4 — The Rough Draft
. . . the put-it-together phase . . . This is the stage at which you say, *"Okay, I've got thoughts and groups of ideas and phrases. I have thought about which of these may fit together. Now . . . write!"* Start putting those words together into phrases, those phrases together into lines or sentences, those sentences together into paragraphs.

Stage 5 — Author's Review
. . . the author's chance to get the writing out into the light and see how it looks and hear how it sounds . . . Read it to yourself (out loud, if possible), and ask . . . *Does it make sense? Does it say what I intended? Do I like it? Is it smooth and clear? Are the ideas in the right order? Are there any words or pieces missing?*

Stage 6 — Sharing for Response
. . . a time for trading pieces, or reading to a small group, or sharing with the teacher for the purpose of getting reactions, questions, suggestions, praise, and ideas for improvements

Stage 7 — Editing and Revising
. . . the changing, fixing stage . . . including anything from reshuffling or replacing words to reworking whole pieces . . . After you have reviewed your own work and have gotten some responses from others, then you can make the changes that need to be made.

Stage 8 — The Mechanics Check
. . . the time to inspect your first draft for spelling, grammar, mechanical, and structural errors or weaknesses . . . This might be a good time to get help from an adult or older student.

Stage 9 — The Final Copy
. . . the writing of the final draft—making use of your ideas for changes and the suggestions others have made . . . When you finish this, you'll learn about the satisfaction and surprise that comes with the polishing of a product.

Stage 10 — Presenting
. . . the sharing, showing-off, or publishing part . . . the chance to use your written words to communicate with other persons. In some way, every finished piece should be made public if the author chooses.

EDITOR'S CHECKLIST

___ Have you chosen a variety of interesting words?

___ Have you gotten rid of repetitive words?

___ Have you gotten rid of dull or overused words?

___ Have you used the most specific, colorful, and interesting words you know?

___ Have you clearly made your main point?

___ Does each paragraph contain sentences that follow the same idea?

___ Do you have plenty of good details about each idea?

___ Do you have any details that are not really related to the topic?

___ Are your sentences and ideas held together by interesting connections?

___ Do you have a variety of sentence lengths and structures?

___ Are your sentences or lines in an order that makes sense?

___ Do you have any sentences that say the same thing as other sentences?

___ Do you have too many sentences that start the same way?

___ Do you have an interesting, reader-catching beginning?

___ Is the middle of the piece clear and interesting?

___ Do you have a strong ending?

___ Did you accomplish your purpose?

___ Did you write for the audience you intended?

___ Read your piece aloud. Do the sentences flow well? Does it sound pleasing?

___ Did you write in a way that will cause the readers to react the way you wanted?

___ Does your writing have excitement or passion that will "draw in" the reader?

___ Did you proofread for:

    ___ Spelling?

    ___ Punctuation?

    ___ Capitalization?

    ___ Incomplete or run-on sentences?

    ___ Words forgotten or skipped or out of order?

GOOD! Then your writing is ready to show off!

WRITING
SKILLS TEST

Questions 1–15 are worth 1 point each.

For questions 1–2, circle the letter of the most precise word for each blank.

1. The elephant _____ along heavily in the parade.
   a. pranced
   b. skipped
   c. slid
   d. lumbered
   e. walked

2. Jana's best friend was _____ by her sudden and mysterious disappearance.
   a. amused
   b. bored
   c. troubled
   d. satisfied

For questions 3 & 4, circle the letter of the word that is most effective for each blank.

3. Someone or something is _____ in the dark shadows, staring out at me with piercing eyes.
   a. hiding
   b. lurking
   c. standing
   d. playing

4. The sunset threw a _____ orange glow across the rippling lake.
   a. glamorous
   b. spectacular
   c. nice
   d. cute

Circle the letter(s) of the correct answer(s).

5. Which example shows an active voice?
   a. The peppers on my sandwich were very hot and spicy.
   b. The spicy peppers bit my tongue.
   c. Pepper juice was spicy on my tongue.

6. Which sentence(s) contain(s) a comparison that is a metaphor and not a simile?
   a. My little sister is a peach of a kid.
   b. This homework is going as slowly as an opera.
   c. Little twin brothers are like double hurricanes.

7. Which sentence(s) contain(s) a simile?
   a. Tom is as salty as a potato chip.
   b. Life is like a puzzle with some of the pieces missing.
   c. My dad's meat loaf tastes like sawdust.
   d. The teakettle hisses at me.

8. Which sentence does NOT contain a metaphor?
   a. The raging river gobbles up boats and swallows them whole.
   b. The wind is a playful kitten.
   c. Math is as slippery as wet spaghetti.

9. Which mood would these words help to set?
   hurry, scurry, fast,
   zip, bustle, quick,
   dart, dash, race
   a. curious
   b. playful
   c. quiet
   d. rushing

10. Which would be a **persuasive** piece of writing?
    a. advertisement convincing someone to buy a new basketball shoe
    b. wild imaginative tale about the future
    c. description of an unusual character
    d. directions for building a kite

11. Which would be an **expository** piece?
    a. a tall tale
    b. an explanation of how you earn interest on your savings account at the bank
    c. a poster encouraging you to try the new lemon liver yogurt
    d. a description of a surfing trip

Name _____

12. Which sentence does NOT contain personification?
    a. The vacuum cleaner will chase you until it gobbles the socks off your feet!
    b. I'm sure that doughnut is calling me!
    c. Trees flutter in the soft spring wind.

13. Which sentence appeals to your sense of hearing?
    a. The scream of the red sirens splits through the black night.
    b. The flashing ambulance lights make my eyes squeeze shut.
    c. My heart pounds wildly in my chest as I wait for the ambulance.

14. Which sentence creates a strong visual image?
    a. The moon is not shining tonight.
    b. Last night's moon shimmered like a slice of silver ribbon in a black sky.
    c. What is it like to walk on the moon?

15. Which sentence does NOT create a strong visual image?
    a. Dripping red juices slowly slide across the road from the wrecked tomato truck.
    b. Fluffy, sugary, golden meringue tops the thick, yellow, lemon cream of the pie.
    c. The cracking and popping sound of her gum hurt my ears.

For each writing task below, follow the directions given. (Worth 5 points each.)

Task 1: Number these sentences (1–7) in an order that makes sense.
____ When it was over, we found our car in the neighbor's swimming pool.
____ Our car was hurled across the street like a plastic toy.
____ The tornado struck at dawn.
____ Suddenly the roar stopped and everything was still.
____ Slowly, we crept out of the shelter.
____ We hurried into the shelter.
____ A whirling, black funnel headed straight for our house.

Task 2: Replace each ordinary word with a more colorful or interesting word. Write a new word above the underlined word.

It was a bad idea to ride the roller coaster when I was feeling sick. The Triple Loop looked scary. Once I got on, my stomach hurt as the roller coaster moved up and down and went from side to side. I have never felt so awful!

Task 3: Write a more active word above each underlined word.
1. The parade went on for four miles.
2. Did you really have six eclairs for lunch?
3. Don't you think she was on the trampoline too long?

Task 4: Rewrite the following sentences to make the meaning clear.
1. Sitting on the top shelf of the closet, I found an old sandwich.

2. We heard about the robber who was caught on the radio.

Task 5: Cross out any unneeded or repetitive ideas.
1. She totally ate the whole pizza.
2. Jason drew seven three-sided triangles in his geometry design.
3. In my opinion, I think that snowboards are not at all dangerous even a bit.

Name ____

Task 6: Write a strong beginning for one of these topics.

- learning to tame a lion
- a dog who can read
- a strange disappearance
- lizards who can dance
- a visit with Bigfoot
- a shocking letter
- an accident
- a terrible flood
- a memory

_____

_____

_____

Task 7: Write a strong ending for one of these topics.

- an earthquake
- a person to avoid
- a place never to go
- a wild hockey game
- a mystery
- a case of green earlobes
- a person to meet
- an embarrassing moment

_____

_____

_____

Task 8: Circle the examples of figurative language in this letter.

Dear Genoa,

You are one bad apple. I am so burned up at you! I went out on a limb to help you with a problem, and now you've let the cat out of the bag about my secret. I thought I could trust you not to spill the beans. Your goose is cooked, girl! No matter how hard you try, I don't think you'll be able to get your foot out of your mouth any time soon.

Sincerely,
Your mad as a hatter ex-friend

Task 9: Write a clear, complete, interesting sentence about one of these topics.

- a bothersome bumblebee
- a wild thunderstorm
- a dark, spooky night
- a slithery snake
- a disappointment
- a tough science test

_____

_____

_____

Task 10: Choose one of the people below, and write two good questions that you would ask him or her.

- someone who had been locked in a refrigerator
- a heart surgeon
- a gorilla trainer
- a Supreme Court justice
- someone who climbed Mt. Everest
- someone who rode a roller coaster for 14 days straight

1. _____

_____

_____

2. _____

_____

_____

Task 11: Write a good headline for this news article.

_____

_____

_____

A man was found wandering on Main Street last night wearing tattered socks and no shoes. He was also missing his shirt, hat, glasses, the left leg of his pants, and his memory. He did not remember anything after seeing an approaching tornado. Police are searching for his family. Anyone having information about his possible identity, call the city police at 555-2222.

Name _____

Task 12: Rewrite the conversation from the cartoon. Write it in a paragraph that includes dialogue. Use correct punctuation for the dialogue.

_____

_____

_____

_____

_____

Editing task 13 is worth 10 points.

TASK 13: Correct the spelling, punctuation, capitalization, and grammar in the following letter. Also, eliminate excess words or phrases. Cross out the errors and write the corrections above each line.

Dear editor

In my opinion, I beleeve that the new minature golf corse which the city has built owned by the city should change its rules. It does not make sens to refuse kids under 18 to come unless they are with adults I thought the city bilt this corse to atract kids and give them something good to do in the evenings. this is a wunderful activity for kids, but you are keeping them away. Most teenagers want to go out for an activity with their friends, not their parents Whose bad idea was this! I protest I hope this rule will be changed soon

Sincerely,

Adam

Writing task 14 is worth 15 points.

Task 14: Write a description, story, or tall tale to go along with the picture. Make sure your piece of writing has:
- a good title
- a strong beginning
- a strong middle
- a strong ending
- details to explain the main idea

_____

_____

_____

_____

_____

_____

_____

_____

_____

_____

_____

_____

_____

_____

Name _____

ANSWER KEY

SKILLS TEST

1. d
2. c
3. b
4. b
5. b
6. a
7. a, b, c
8. c
9. d
10. a
11. b
12. c
13. a
14. b
15. c

Writing Tasks

Answers will vary on most of the writing tasks. There are no right or wrong answers for Tasks 2, 3, 6, 7, 9, 10, 11, 12, and 14. Answers may vary some on Tasks 4, 5, and 13.
Award points to students based on:
- how thoroughly they completed the task
- if they followed directions
- the mechanical correctness of their writing

Task 1: order—7, 4, 1, 5, 6, 3, 2

Task 4: Answers may vary somewhat.
1. I found an old sandwich sitting on top of the shelf in the closet.
2. On the radio, we heard about the robber who was caught.

Task 5: These words may be crossed out.
1. totally or whole
2. three-sided
3. In my opinion, or I think
   not at all, or even a bit

Task 8: Figurative language includes
bad apple, burned up, out on a limb, let the cat out of the bag, spill the beans, goose is cooked, get your foot out of your mouth, mad as a hatter

Task 13: Words that students eliminate may vary. Statements or words in ( ) are not necessary and should be deleted. Corrected paragraph should read:
Dear Editor:
(In my opinion,) I believe that the new miniature golf course (which the city has built) owned by the city should change its rules. It does not make sense to refuse kids under 18 to come unless they are with adults. I thought the city built this course to attract kids and give them something good to do in the evenings. This is a wonderful activity for kids, but you are keeping them away. Most teenagers want to go out (for an activity) with their friends, not their parents! Whose bad idea was this? (I protest!) I hope this rule will be changed soon.
                              Sincerely,
                              Adam

SKILLS EXERCISES

For most of the activities, the answers will vary. Check to see that students have completed the tasks with reasonable responses that fit the directions given. Answers are listed below for the pages that have specific answers or answers that may vary only somewhat.

page 12

Answers will vary, but the following words are the least active ones in the sentences and should most likely be replaced:
1. came, went
2. walked
3. came
4. were
5. ate
6. looked
7. were
8. came
9. were
10. used

page 13

There are many possible answers for most items. These are some possibilities:
1. threatening (or deafening)
2. damp
3. perilous
4. plummets
5. foolish
6. jagged
7. sturdy
8. rushing
9. treacherous
10. fearless
11. moldy
12. nervous
13. cramped
14. awestruck
15. swirling
16. battered

page 19

Answers may vary some, but should be along these lines:

1. While I was riding The Corkscrew for the third time, a stomachache bothered me.
2. When I was a child, my dad took me on roller coasters every weekend.
3. I'll write in the magazine about the pirates who robbed ships.
4. The wind picked up while we were riding The Plunge.
5. The clown sold cold ice cream bars with sprinkles to the children.
6. The manager banned some teenagers from The Terror Train because they broke the rules.
7. The kids worried that their mother would never recover after fainting on the ride through The Python's Den.

8. After their teacher fell off her seat into The Raging River, the students tried to pull her back into the raft.

9. To save money for a day at the amusement park, Tim and Tom went to work for Mrs. Burton cleaning her garage.

10. Last, I visited the very scary Haunted Mansion which was located beside the ticket booth.

pages 20–27

For most of the activities, the answers will vary. Check to see that students have completed the tasks with reasonable responses that fit the directions given.

page 28

Answers will vary, but students should include details similar to the following examples:

Sahara

Catch a glimpse of a mirage. Enjoy cool drinks in a green oasis. Find out what it's really like to ride on a camel. Find plants and animals that survive on very little water. Watch the wind create dunes and patterns in the sand.

Amazon

Enjoy some unusually fine fishing. Get some close-up photos of big crocodiles. See some of the most beautiful tropical birds in the world. You might catch a glimpse of a cheetah or an anaconda. Experience a lush tropical rain forest first hand.

Antarctica

See for yourself the most mammoth ice shelf in the world. The sun will shine until midnight!. Spend a whole day watching playful penguins. Climb on glaciers and photograph icebergs.

pages 30–31

Unrelated details are:

1. Judge Laws had just had a turkey club sandwich for lunch when the case began. Judge Laws coughed from a bad cold.

2. Anthony was wearing a suit and tie in court today.

3. Mrs. Grundy lives in a pink house on Blossom Street. She told the judge that her grandchildren visit her every Saturday. Mrs. Grundy has a cat.

4. He also buys a dozen sticky buns and two pumpkin pies.

5. Arthur Rush makes his living designing socks for the Shoes & Socks Emporium. Mr. Rush drives a Mustang and Judge Laws drives a Volkswagen.

6. The city has a population of 21,000. Her house has three stories.

page 32

There may be more than one sequence of sentences that would make a clear report. Here is one possibility:

Farmer McCully called 911 at noon to report a loud roaring sound that was shaking the earth near his farm. I was in the area, so I raced to the farm. When I arrived, I found Farmer McCully's pigs looking shocked. Just then, I heard terrible screaming in addition to the loud roaring sound. I looked up in the sky toward the terrible noise. Unbelievably, a bathtub was whirling through the air. A young man in the tub was screaming for his life. Fortunately, the tub landed safely in the pig pen. No one was hurt, not even the pigs.

pages 40–41

Letter from Robert Lozenge:
making too many bones; a frog in my throat; raining cats and dogs; I'm pretty burned up; off my rocker.
   ANSWERS: barking up the wrong tree; up a creek; in the pink
Letter from Veronica Lobes:
tongue-tied; stick my neck out; exercising my head off; pulling your leg; down in the dumps
   ANSWERS: I'll be a monkey's uncle!; takes the cake; blows my mind; I am stumped; driving you up a wall; quick as a wink
Letter from Sam Troubles:
straight from the horse's mouth; fit to be tied; from sunup to sundown; a chip off the old block!
   ANSWERS: crying your eyes out; pass the buck; you scream your head off; burn rubber

pages 52–53

Errors are underlined and corrected below. Statements in ( ) are not necessary and could be deleted. Students may make other editing decisions.

Dear Editor:

Why are you saying negative things in your magazine about the new city tax on food in all the restaurants? What is your problem? The tax is for a good cause. Just a small amount on each meal adds up to thousands of dollars for our parks. This is really good for kids. It gives us a wonderful swimming pool, too. This is a small price to pay for so much good stuff. (The cost is really pretty small.) And our restaurants have good food. If I buy a $4.00 sandwich, it only costs 20¢ extra for the tax. Even if someone gets a very expensive meal—say $50.00, the 5% tax still only adds $2.50. That's not bad! It gives us nice, clean places to play soccer and softball.
            Sincerely,
            Whitney

Dear Editor:

No one has asked the kids! Everyone in the town is talking about year-round school. All the adults keep having hearings and meetings to discuss this. Some committee is making a plan for school to go through the summer. I am really mad! (I am on a dance team.) If something is being planned that changes our whole lives, especially taking away our summers, it is unfair to go ahead without talking to the students. We have opinions, too. We should be the ones to decide this, since it is all about our education.
            Sincerely,
            Madder Than A Wet Hen

page 54

Answers will vary.